Toad of Toad Hall a Comedy

abridged by Martin Coles and Christine Hall

Introduction

The famous book on which this play is based is called *The Wind in the Willows*, by Kenneth Grahame. It was written in 1908. Kenneth Grahame was born in Edinburgh, but when he was young his mother died of scarlet fever, and he was sent to live with his grandmother in the village of Cookham Dene in England, the main setting of *The Wind in the Willows*. Grahame originally wrote parts of *The Wind in the Willows* in letters to his young son Alistair.

In 1929 A.A. Milne, who was already well known for his Winnie the Pooh stories, turned the book into a play called *Toad of Toad Hall*. The main characters in the story are the shy little Mole, clever Ratty, Badger, and crazy Toad. They talk and behave like humans, but they all have typical animal habits.

The story of Toad of Toad Hall

Toad is obsessed with cars, but he crashes them regularly.
Badger, Mole and Rat try to persuade Toad to give up his
obsession, fearing for his life. When he refuses, they hold him
hostage in Badger's house in the frightening Wild Wood until
he can be "cured" of his "illness". Toad escapes by tricking
Rat, but eventually his motoring lands him in prison.
However he escapes from prison too, disguised as a
washerwoman. But while Toad is in prison Toad Hall is
invaded by stoats and weasels. Toad and his friends fight off
the enemy to recapture Toad Hall.

Scenes from Toad of Toad Hall

Act 2

Act 4

Characters

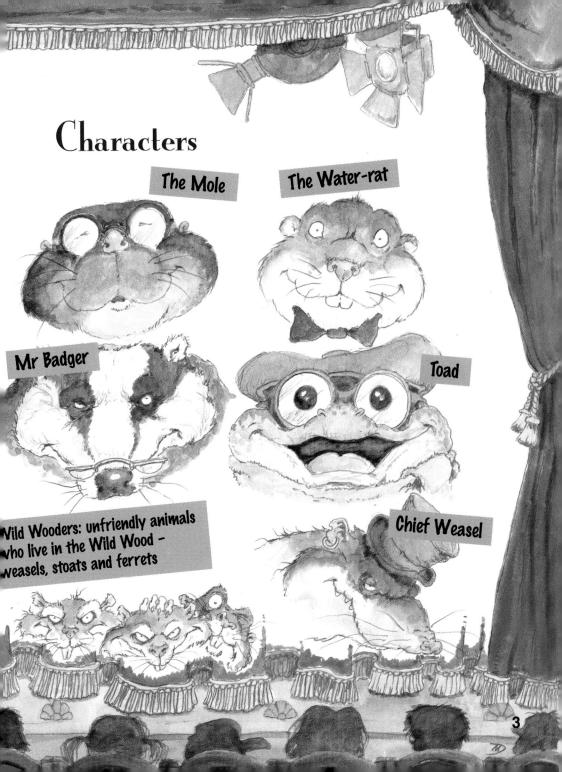

The Mole

The Water-rat

Mr Badger

Toad

Wild Wooders: unfriendly animals who live in the Wild Wood – weasels, stoats and ferrets

Chief Weasel

Act 2 Scene 1

The Wild Wood

The middle of the Wild Wood. It is an awesome place in the moonlight, with the snow thick upon the ground, cold, silent, threatening. You feel that there are hidden watchers behind the trees, waiting to jump out at you. There is a sudden rustling … and then silence. A twig cracks. Somebody is breathing …

MOLE Ratty! (*in sudden panic*) What's that? Pah! It's nothing! I'm not frightened! I do wish Ratty were here. He's so comforting, is Ratty.

He seems to hear the sound of mocking laughter

What's that? Ratty always said, "Don't go into the Wild Wood." That's what he always said. "Not by yourself," he said. "It isn't safe," he said. "We never do," he said. That's what Ratty said. But I thought I knew better. There he was, dear old Rat, dozing in front of the fire, and I thought if I just slipped out, just to see what the Wild Wood was like –

He breaks off suddenly and darts round, fearing an attack from behind. There is nothing

I should be safer up against a tree. Why didn't I think of that before? Ratty would have thought of it – he's so wise. Oh, Ratty, I wish you were here. It's so much more friendly with two.

His head droops wearily on his chest as he falls asleep

A VOICE (*from far off*) Moly! Moly!

MOLE (*waking up suddenly*) What's that?

A VOICE Moly!

MOLE (*frightened*)	Who is it?
A VOICE	Moly! Moly! Moly! Where are you? It's me – it's old Rat!

Rat appears; a lantern in his hand, a couple of pistols in his belt, and a cudgel over his shoulder

MOLE (*almost in tears*)	
	Oh, Rat! Oh, Rat!
RAT (*patting him on the back*)	
	There, there, there!
MOLE	Oh, Ratty, I've been so frightened, you can't think.
RAT	I know, I know. You shouldn't have gone and done it, Mole. I did my best to keep you from it. We River-Bankers hardly ever come, except in couples.
MOLE	But you've come by yourself. Ah, but then that's because you're so brave.

RAT	It isn't just bravery, it's knowing. There are a hundred things you have to know, which we understand about, and you don't as yet. Of course if you're Badger, it's different.
MOLE	Surely the brave Mr Toad wouldn't mind coming here by himself?
RAT (*laughing*)	Old Toad? He wouldn't show his face here alone, not for a whole hatful of guineas, Toad wouldn't.
MOLE	Oh, Rat! It is comforting to hear somebody laugh again.
RAT	Well, shall we start?
MOLE	Oh, Ratty. I don't know how to tell you, but I can't, I simply *can't* go all that way now.
RAT	Tired?
MOLE	Aching all over. Oh, Ratty, do forgive me. I feel as if I must just sit here for ever and ever and ever, and I'm not a bit frightened now you're with me – and – and I think I want to go to sleep.

Act 2
Scene 1

Toad of
Toad Hall
– a comedy

STALLS

RAT	That's all right. But we can't stop *here*.

He looks round about him

Suppose we go and dig in that mound there, and see if we can't make some sort of a shelter out of the snow and the wind, and have a good rest. And then start for home a bit later on. How's that?

MOLE (*meekly*)   Just as you like, Rat. Come on, then.

Rat leads the way to the mound, and Mole, following, trips up suddenly and falls over with a squeal

MOLE   Oh, my leg! Oh, my poor shin! Oo!

RAT   Poor old Mole, you don't seem to be having much luck today, do you? What is it? Hurt your shin? Let's have a look at it.

MOLE   I must have tripped over a stump or something. Oh my! Oh *my*!

RAT   It's a very clean cut. That was never done by a stump. Looks like the sharp edge of something metal. Funny!

MOLE   Well, never mind what done it. It hurts just the same whatever did it.

RAT   Wait a moment.

He begins scratching in the snow

MOLE   What is it?

RAT   I thought so!

7

MOLE	What *is* it?
RAT	Come and see.
MOLE (*hobbling up*)	Hallo, a door-scraper! How very careless of somebody!
RAT	But don't you see what it means?
MOLE (*sitting down again and rubbing his shin*)	Of course I see what it means. It means that some *very* forgetful person has left his door-scraper lying about in the middle of the Wild Wood just where it's sure to trip everybody up. Somebody ought to write to him about it.
RAT	Oh, Mole, how stupid you are.

He begins scratching busily again

There! What's that?

MOLE (*examining it closely*)	It looks like a door-mat.
RAT	It is a door-mat. And what does *that* tell you?
MOLE	Nothing, Rat, nothing. Who ever heard of a door-mat telling anyone anything? They simply don't do it. They are not that sort at all. They – what have you found *now*?

Rat has now disclosed a solid-looking little door, with a brass plate on it

RAT (*proudly*)	There!

He fetches the lantern and holds it up to the plate

What do you read there?

MOLE (*awestruck*)	"Mr Badger" … Rat!
RAT (*proudly*)	What do you think of *that*?

Act 2
Scene 1

Toad of
Toad Hall
– a comedy

STALLS

MOLE	Rat, you're a wonder, that's what you are! I see it all now. You argued it out step by step from the moment when I fell and cut my shin, and you looked at the cut, and your majestic mind said to itself, "Door-scraper". Did it stop there? No. Your powerful brain went on working. It said to itself –
RAT (*impatiently*)	Yes, yes, well now, let's –
MOLE	Your powerful brain said to itself, "Where there's a scraper, there must be a mat."
RAT	Quite so.
MOLE	"I have noticed before," said the wise Mr Rat, "that where there's a scraper there must be a mat." And did you stop *there?* No. Your intellect still went on working. It said grandly to itself, "Where there's a door-mat there must be a door."
RAT	Exactly. And now that we've found it –
MOLE	You know, Rat, you're simply wasted here amongst us fellows. If I only had your head –
RAT	But as you haven't, I suppose you are going to sit on the snow and *talk* all night. Now wake up a bit and hang on to this bell-pull, while I hammer.
MOLE (*sleepily*)	Oh, all right! Said the wise Mr. Rat, "I have often heard tell that where there's a bell-pull there *must* be a bell."

He hangs on to the bell-pull, while Rat hammers on the door with his cudgel. Down in Mr Badger's house a deep-toned bell responds.

9

Act 2 Scene 2

SCENE — Badger's underground home. There is a big open fireplace and an armchair in which the owner can sit with The Times, *and is now doing so. The front door bell rings — again and again. Grumbling to himself, Badger gets to his feet, and goes to the door.*

BADGER	*All right, all right!* What is it, who is it?
He opens the front door	
	Speak up!
RAT	Hallo, Badger! It's me, Rat, and my friend Mole, and we've lost our way in the snow, and Mole's that tired.
BADGER	Well, well, well! Rat and his friend Mole!
He brings them in	
	Come along in, both of you, at once. Why, you must be perished! Well, I never! Lost in the snow! And your friend that tired! Well, well! And in the Wild Wood at this time of night! Come along in. There's a good fire here, and supper and everything.

Act 2
Scene 2

Toad of
Toad Hall
– a comedy

STALLS

MOLE   Oo, I say!

He nudges the Rat in an anticipatory sort of way

BADGER   Now what will you do first? Toast your toes a bit? Or supper now, and toast your toes afterwards? It's all ready. I was expecting one or two friends might drop in.

MOLE (*shyly*)   I think I should like supper at once, please, Mr Badger.

BADGER   That's right, Mole. Sensible animal. And what about you, Rat?

RAT (*standing with his back to the fire, as an old friend should*)
        Just as you like. Fine old place this, isn't it, Mole?

MOLE (*already among the plates*) Grand.

Rat fetches himself a sandwich and gets his back to the fire again. Badger, in an armchair, beams upon them kindly

BADGER (*solemnly, after a silence broken only by the noise of eating*)
        I've been wanting to see you fellows, because I have heard very grave reports of our mutual friend, Toad.

RAT (*sadly*)   Oh, Toad!

MOLE   Tut-tut-tut.

BADGER   Is his case as hopeless as one has heard?

RAT   Going from bad to worse – that's all you can say about him, isn't it, Mole?

MOLE   Mmm! (*swallowing hastily*)

11

RAT	Another smash-up only last week, and a bad one. You see, since he's got this motor craze, he will insist on driving himself, and he's hopelessly incapable. He's convinced he's the greatest driver ever, and nobody can teach him anything. And so it goes on.
MOLE	And so it goes on.
BADGER (*gloomily*)	And so it goes on! How many has he had?
RAT	Cars or smashes? Oh well, it's the same thing with Toad. The last was the seventh.
MOLE	He's been in hospital three times, and as for the fines he's had to pay –
RAT	Toad's rich, we all know, but he's not a millionaire. Killed or ruined, it will be one or the other with Toad.
BADGER	Alas, alas!
RAT (*to Badger*)	Oughtn't we to *do* something? We're his friends.
BADGER	Yes. You're right. The hour has come.
MOLE (*anxiously*)	What hour?
BADGER	Whose hour, you should say. Toad's hour. The hour of Toad.
RAT (*quietly*)	Well done, Badger. I knew you'd feel that way too.
MOLE (*firmly*)	*We'll* teach him to be a sensible Toad.

Act 2
Scene 2

Toad of
Toad Hall
– a comedy

STALLS

BADGER	At any moment another new and exceptionally powerful motor car will arrive at Toad Hall for approval or return. We must be up and doing 'ere it is too late.
RAT	That's right, Badger. We'll rescue the poor unhappy animal! We'll convert him!
BADGER	The first step is to get him here and reason with him.
RAT	How to get him, that's the problem –
BADGER (*gravely*)	Let us apply our minds to it.

They apply their minds. Suddenly the bell rings loudly

BADGER	Whoever's that?

Badger shuffles off to the door, and as he opens it, Toad falls into his arms, panting with fear

RAT (*in surprise*)	Why, it's Toad! What's the matter?

Toad, supported by Badger, falls limply into a chair and sits there panting

Another accident?

Toad shakes his head

That's something.

TOAD (*still panting*)	Ah, Ratty, my dear old Ratty, and my good friend Mole, how badly I seemed to need your help just now! What would I not have given to have had you by my side. As it was, I had to do the best I could without you. Fortunately it was enough. But as you see, it has exhausted me!
RAT	What's happened? Wild Wooders?

13

TOAD (*warming to it*) An unfortunate breakdown in my car – a loose nut, some trifling mishap – left me stranded at the edge of the wood, far from home. I bethought me of my good friend Mr Badger; he would put me up for the night. As I came whistling through the wood, thinking nothing of danger, I was suddenly seized upon by a gang of rascally ferrets. I set about them light-heartedly – at the most there were no more than a dozen of them – when suddenly, to my horror, they were reinforced by a posse of scoundrelly weasels. It was then, Ratty – and my dear friend Mole – that I wished I had your assistance. Twelve of the rascals, yes (*he is now standing up, legs straddled, and enjoying himself immensely*) but twenty-four of them is a different matter. If only you and Mole could have taken a couple of them off my hands, there might have been a different story to tell. As it was, a rearguard action was forced upon me. Step by step –

He realises a faint hostile something in the air, particularly from the direction of Badger. He goes on less confidently

Step by step –

He looks from one to the other, hoping for a little encouragement, but the atmosphere is now really terrible. He makes a last desperate effort

Step by step –

BADGER (*solemnly*)	Won't you sit down again, Toad?
TOAD (*meekly*)	Thank you.
BADGER (*to Rat*)	The moment has come, I think, don't you?
RAT	I think so.
BADGER (*to Mole*)	You agree?
MOLE	Yes. (*He sighs*)
TOAD (*uneasily*)	I say, you fellows, what's all this –

He catches Badger's eye and is silent again

BADGER (*solemnly*)	The question I wish to ask you now is this. At the beginning of the breathless story of adventure to which we have just been listening, you mentioned (*he pauses dramatically*) a motor car. Is it indeed a fact that your eighth motor car is now in as fragmentary a condition as the previous seven?
TOAD (*sulkily*)	I had a little accident.
BADGER	Thank you.
(*To Rat*)	Then I think in that case we may begin the treatment?
TOAD	I say, you fellows –
BADGER	Toad!
RAT	It's all for your own good, Toady old man. We've been talking it over for hours. Might as well take it quietly.
MOLE	We don't like doing it, Toad, really we don't. It's only because we are so fond of you.

Rat and Mole remove Toad's goggles

BADGER	Now then, Toad. You've disregarded all the warnings we've given you and you're getting us animals a bad name in the district by your furious driving and your smashes and your rows with the police. We have decided that it is time we saved you from yourself. I am going to make one more effort to bring you to reason. You will come with me into my study, and there you will hear some facts about yourself. Come!
TOAD (*meekly*)	Yes, Badger. Thank you, Badger.

Badger and Toad go out together

RAT	That's no good! Talking to Toad will never cure him. He'll *say* anything.
MOLE	Yes. (*He sighs*)
RAT	We must *do* something.

The door opens again and Badger comes in, leading by the paw a very dejected Toad

BADGER (*kindly*)	Sit down there, Toad. My friends, I am pleased to inform you that Toad has at last seen the error of his ways. He is truly sorry for his misguided conduct in the past, and he has undertaken to give up motor cars entirely and for ever in the future. I have his solemn promise to that effect.
MOLE (*eagerly*)	Oh, Toad, I *am* glad!
RAT (*doubtfully*)	H'm!
BADGER	There is only one thing which remains to be done. Toad, I want you solemnly to repeat before your friends here what you fully admitted to me in the study just now. First, you are sorry for what you have done and see the folly of it all?

There is an anxious silence

Act 2
Scene 2

Toad of
Toad Hall
– a comedy

STALLS

TOAD (*suddenly*)   No! I'm *not* sorry. And it wasn't folly at all. It was simply glorious.

BADGER (*horrified*)   What?

MOLE   Toady!

RAT   I thought so.

BADGER   You back-sliding animal, didn't you tell me just now in there –

TOAD   Oh yes, yes, in *there*. I'd have said anything in *there*. You're so eloquent, dear Badger, and so moving, and so convincing, and put all your points so frightfully well – you can do what you like with me in *there*. But, thinking it over out *here*, I see that I am not a bit sorry really! On the contrary, I faithfully promise that the very first motor car I see – Poop-poop, off I go in it!

RAT (*to Mole*)   I told you so.

BADGER   Very well then. Since you won't yield to persuasion, we'll try what force can do. You'll stay with me, Toad, until a cure has been effected. My friends, Rat and Mole, will also stay with me and help me to look after you. It's going to be a tedious business, but we will see it out.

He takes down a large key from the wall, and picking up the lantern leads the way to the guest-chamber

Bring him along.

The procession goes slowly, and on Toad's part reluctantly, out.

17

Act 2 Scene 3

SCENE – Badger's home some weeks later. Toad has arranged three chairs in a hopeful representation of a motor car. He sits on the front one, grasping an imaginary wheel, changing imaginary gears, and making appropriate noises. All of a sudden the chairs are strewn about and Toad lies panting in the wreckage. Badger lifts an eye, glances at him and goes on with his paper. Mole comes in. He looks at Toad.

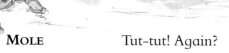

MOLE	Tut-tut! Again?
BADGER (*reading his paper*)	The third crash this morning. There seems to be a good deal of traffic on the road today.
MOLE	Poor old Toad!
BADGER	I always warned you, my dear Mole, that in these cases the poison takes a long time to work itself out of the system. But we're improving; we're improving daily. Let me see. It's Rat's turn to be on guard this morning, isn't it?
MOLE	Yes. (*Helping Toad up*) Lean on me, old fellow. That's right. Lie down a bit.

He assists him towards a camp bed in the corner of the room

	You'll be better directly.
TOAD (*weakly*)	Thank you, my dear friend, thank you.
MOLE	That's all right, Toady. We'll soon get you well.

BADGER	What do you say to a bit of a ramble along the hedgerows, Mole? And there's a new burrow I want to show you. I must say I like being out in this sort of weather.
MOLE (*eagerly*)	Just what I was going to suggest. I wish old Ratty could come too. I suppose –

He looks across at Toad

BADGER	No, no, it wouldn't be safe.
(*In a whisper*)	Toad's quiet now, and when he is quiet, then he's at his artfullest. I know him.
MOLE	Yes, I suppose so. But it's such an exciting sort of day. Rat would love it so.

Enter Rat

RAT	Hallo, you fellows, not off yet?
BADGER	Just going.
He gets up	Toad's quiet now. But keep an eye on him. I don't trust him.
RAT	That's all right.
MOLE (*quietly to Rat*)	I believe he's worse than Badger thinks. Look after him well, poor old Toad.
RAT	That's all right.
BADGER (*at the door*)	Coming, Mole?
MOLE	Coming. Poor old Ratty, it is a shame being kept in like this. Still, we all have our turns.
RAT	Of course we do. Good luck to you.
MOLE	Goodbye!
BADGER	Are you coming, Mole?
MOLE	Coming! Goodbye! Goodbye, Toad!

They go out

RAT	Well, how are you today, old chap?
TOAD (*faintly*)	Thank you so much, dear Ratty. It is good of you to inquire.
RAT	Now, old boy, we're going to have a jolly morning together, so jump up, and I'll do my best to amuse you.
TOAD	Dear, kind Rat, how little you realise my condition, and how very far I am from jumping up now – if ever. In fact I wonder if I could bother you, you have been too kind already.
RAT	Why, what is it? You know we'd do anything for you, all of us.
TOAD	Then could I beg you, for the last time probably, to step round to the village as quickly as possible – even now it may be too late – fetch the doctor.
RAT (*surprised*)	But what do you want a doctor for?
TOAD	Surely you have noticed – But no, why should you? Tomorrow, indeed, you may be saying to yourself, "Oh, if only I had noticed sooner! If only I had *done* something! Too late, too late!" … Forget that I asked.
RAT (*alarmed*)	Look here, old man, of course I'll fetch a doctor to you, if you really want one. But it hasn't come to that yet. You're imagining. Now let's talk about something more cheerful.

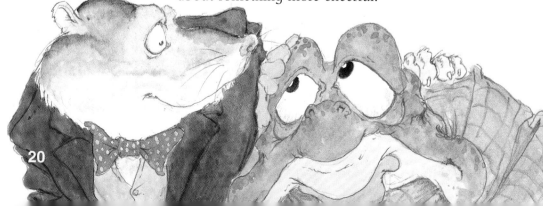

Act 2
Scene 3

Toad of
Toad Hall
– a comedy

STALLS

TOAD (*with an angelic expression*) I fear, dear friend, that talk can do little in a case like this – or doctors either, for that matter. By the way – while you are in the village – *would* you mind asking my lawyer to step up so I can arrange my Will? Thank you, my dear fellow, thank you. You will not be forgotten.

He closes his eyes

RAT   A lawyer! He *must* be bad.

(*Aloud*)   All right, Toad, I'll go.

He makes his preparations to go out, glancing from time to time at the unconscious Toad as he does so. Then a brilliant idea occurs to him

RAT (*loudly*)   I'm going now, Toad.

TOAD (*faintly, his eyes closed*) Thank you, thank you!

RAT   I'll bring the doctor and the lawyer, and we'll be back as quickly as we can.

TOAD   You're a good fellow, Ratty.

RAT   Goodbye, old boy. Keep your spirits up.

TOAD   Goodbye!

Humming a tune and making a good deal of noise, Rat goes out. Then very quietly he steals back again and peers round the door. But Toad's illness seems genuine. As Rat's song dies in the distance, Toad opens an eye. Then the other eye. He raises his head and listens. Then with a laugh he jumps up

TOAD (*boastfully*)   Ha, ha, ha! Smart piece of work that! Brain against brute force – and brain came out on the top – as it's bound to do. A worthy fellow, Ratty, with many good qualities, but very little intelligence – and absolutely no education.

He is singing a song as he opens the door. Then with a triumphant "Poop-poop! Poop-poop!" he disappears.

Act 4 Scene 1

SCENE – *Rat's riverside residence. It is something like the cabin of a ship. Rat is busy with a large heap of pistols, swords and cudgels. At one of the portholes the head of Toad appears suddenly.*

TOAD (*from outside*) Help! Help!

RAT (*thoughtfully listening*) Funny! That sounded like Toad's voice.

TOAD Help!

RAT (*turning round*) Toady!

TOAD Give us a hand, Rat. I'm about done.

RAT (*excitedly*) Old Toad!

He seizes hold of him Well, this *is* – What's the matter? No strength left?

TOAD You'll have to pull me in. I'm about done.

RAT That's all right. Got one kick left in you? Good! Well, when I say, "Kick", kick, and I'll pull, and – Now then, ready?

TOAD (*faintly*) Yes.

RAT Then – kick!

Toad kicks. Rat pulls, and Toad tumbles in on the floor

TOAD (*gasping*) Oh! Oh! …

RAT (*helping him up*) Come on, won't you?

TOAD (*faintly*) Thank you, dear Ratty, thank you.

He flops on to the sofa

RAT (*looking at him*) Poor old Toady! And wet as wet … We'll soon have you all right.

TOAD It takes a good deal to put me out, Ratty. Just a passing faintness which might happen to anyone who had been through what *I've* been through.

RAT You've been through a lot, I expect.

Act 4
Scene 1

Toad of
Toad Hall
– a comedy

STALLS

TOAD	Been in prison – got out of it, of course! Stole a horse – rode away on it. Oh, I *am* a smart Toad, and no mistake. Now what do you think my very last exploit was?
RAT (*severely*)	I don't know, Toad. But seeing where it was I found you, and the state you were in, I should say that somebody had dropped you into the river, and then thrown mud at you. It isn't a thing to boast about, really it isn't, Toad.
TOAD	Pah, that was nothing.
RAT (*warningly*)	Toad!
TOAD	Here, hold on a moment. I just want to tell you –
RAT	Toad, will you go upstairs and see if you can make yourself look like a respectable animal again.
TOAD (*with dignity*)	You can hardly realise, Ratty, to whom you are –
RAT	Now stop swaggering and arguing and be off. Badger and Mole will be in directly.
TOAD (*airily*)	Oh, ah! Yes, of course, the Mole and the Badger. What's become of them, the dear fellows? I had forgotten all about them.
RAT (*gravely*)	Well may you ask!
TOAD	Why, what –
RAT	You will hear in good time. Badger himself may prefer to break the news to you. Be off now, and prepare yourself – why, what's the matter?
TOAD (*who has wandered in front of a mirror and is regarding himself with horror*)	Is this glass of yours all right?
RAT	Of course. Why?
TOAD (*meekly*)	You're quite right, Ratty. I'll go and change.

Toad goes out

Rat, left alone, fetches duster, pan and brush, and begins to clean up after Toad, murmuring "Dear, dear!" to himself, and "Well, I never!" While he is so engaged, Badger and Mole come in.

RAT (*eagerly*)   Hallo, here you are! I say, what do you think?

MOLE (*dropping into a chair*) Too tired to think, Ratty, and that's a fact.

RAT   Yes, but —

BADGER (*gruffly*)   Nobody thinks nowadays. That's the trouble. Too much action, not enough thought.

Badger stretches himself on the sofa

RAT   Yes, but —

MOLE (*to Rat*)   He's a bit low, just now. We've had a hard day. He'll be all right directly.

RAT   Yes, but what do you think? Toad's back.

MOLE (*jumping up*) Toad! Back where?

RAT   Here!

MOLE   Where?

RAT (*with a jerk of the head*) Cleaning. You ought to have seen him, Mole. He'd have made you laugh.

MOLE   Has he heard the news?

RAT   Not yet. I said Badger would tell him.

MOLE   Old Toad! He's just in time. Badger thinks it will be tonight!

RAT (*eagerly*)   Not really?

MOLE   Yes. *He* says so.

RAT	I've been polishing up the pistols and cutlasses. They're all ready.
MOLE	Good. We shall want all we can –
BADGER	Rat! Did I hear you say that our young friend Toad had escaped from his noisome dungeon?
RAT	Came in five minutes ago. In such a state.
BADGER	I would speak with him.
RAT	He's just having a wash.
BADGER (*severely*)	This is no time for washing. We have work before us tonight. Hard fighting. Washing can wait. Where do you think *I* should have been if, at the crisis of my life, I had stopped to wash? Where would my father have been if –

Toad comes in, almost his old self

TOAD (*cheerily*)   Hallo, you fellows!

MOLE (*delightedly*)   Toady!

BADGER (*solemnly rising*)

Welcome home,
Toad! Alas!
What am I
saying? Home,
indeed. This
is a poor
homecoming.
Unhappy Toad!

He sinks on to the sofa again

MOLE   Fancy having *you* back!
And today of all days!
To think that you have
escaped from prison, you
clever, intelligent Toad.

TOAD   Clever? Oh, no! I'm not clever, really. Badger
doesn't think so. Rat doesn't think so. I've only
broken out of the strongest prison in England, that's
all. And disguised myself. Clever? Oh dear, no.

RAT   Oh, Toady!

TOAD   Well, I shall be strolling along to Toad Hall. One
does get appreciated at home. Mole, if you'd like
to drop in to coffee one evening, and care to hear
a few of my milder adventures –

MOLE (*sadly*)   Oh, Toady, and you haven't heard!

TOAD   Heard what? Quick, don't spare me! What
haven't I heard?

MOLE   The stoats and the weasels!

Act 4
Scene 1

Toad of
Toad Hall
– a comedy

STALLS

RAT	The Wild Wooders!
MOLE	And how they've been and gone –
RAT	And taken Toad Hall –
MOLE	And been living there ever since –
RAT	Going on simply anyhow –
MOLE	Lying in bed half the day –
RAT	Breakfast at all hours –
MOLE	Eating your grub and drinking your drink –
RAT	And making bad jokes about you –
MOLE	That's what's happened, Toad. And it's no good pretending it hasn't.
RAT	And they're all telling everybody that they've come to Toad Hall to stay for good.
TOAD	Oh, have they! I'll jolly soon see about that!
BADGER	Be quiet, all of you!
They are silent	Toad!
TOAD (*meekly*)	Yes, Badger?
BADGER	When you got into trouble a short time ago, and brought disgrace upon your own name, and shame and sorrow upon your friends, I resolved that on your return from your enforced seclusion, I would take the first opportunity of pointing out to you the folly of your ways.
TOAD (*meekly*)	Yes, Badger. Thank you, Badger.

BADGER	I even went so far as to jot down a few rough notes on the subject. But the moment for all this is past.
TOAD (*humbly*)	Just as you like, Badger, old man.
BADGER	The moment is past, because it is obvious now to everybody here where your folly has brought you. Toad Hall is in the hands of your enemies. Sentries guard it day and night. Unhappy Toad.
TOAD (*bursting into tears*)	Alas, alas! Toad Hall, that desirable riverside residence, in the hands of Stoats and Weasels! This is, indeed, the end of everything!

Toad rolls on to the sofa in his grief

BADGER	Not quite the end. I haven't said my last word yet. Now I'm going to tell you a great secret. We are too few to attack from the front, but there is an underground passage that leads from the River Bank right up into the middle of Toad Hall.

Act 4
Scene 1

Toad of
Toad Hall
– a comedy

STALLS

TOAD (*sitting up brightly*) Oh, nonsense, Badger! I know every inch of Toad Hall inside and out. You've been listening to gossip, that's what you've been doing.

BADGER (*severely*) Right up into the middle of Toad Hall. Your father, who was a particular friend of mine, told me about it.

TOAD This passage. How shall we use it?

BADGER Tonight the Chief Weasel is giving a banquet. It's his birthday. While they are all feasting, careless of the morrow, we four, armed to the teeth, will creep silently, by way of the passage, into the butler's pantry. Armed to the teeth, you and Rat, by one door –

TAT (*looking up*) Yes, Badger.

BADGER And me and Mole by the other –

MOLE Yes, Badger.

BADGER Armed to the teeth we shall –

MOLE Creep out of the pantry –

RAT With our pistols, and swords, and sticks –

BADGER And rush in on them –

TOAD (*ecstatically*) And whack 'em and whack 'em and whack 'em.

BADGER Exactly.

He pats Toad on the back

BADGER Now then, to rest, all of you. We start at nine o'clock, and we must be fresh for it.

He settles down on the sofa

TOAD (*drawing a chair next to Mole*)
  Yes, we must rest.

29

Act 4 Scene 3

SCENE — *The banqueting-room* — *a magnificent apartment* — *in Toad Hall. It being the Chief Weasel's birthday, a banquet is in progress. The hero of the occasion, a laurel wreath on his brow, sits at the head of the main table, his admirers around him. Pressed for a few more words, he rises.*

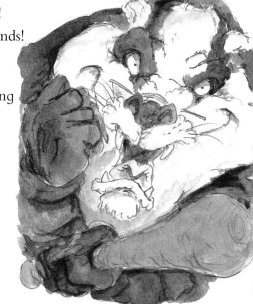

CHIEF WEASEL Friends and fellow animals. Before we part this evening I have one final toast to propose. (*Hear, hear!*) Mr Toad has generously put his entire establishment at our disposal for as long as we like to make use of it. (*Loud laughter.*) But while we are thinking of our good host, Mr Toad, we must not forget our other absent friends — Mr Badger, Mr Rat and Mr Mole. (*Laughter*) From time to time, indeed, of late, we have caught glimpses of them — behind hedges. (*Laughter*) We have seen their back views (*laughter*) — in the distance (*laughter*) — running away. (*Laughter*) Fellow animals, I give you the toast — "Absent Friends!"

ALL (*rising and drinking*) Absent Friends!

A DEEP VOICE OUTSIDE Absent Friends!

ALL (*to each other*) What's that? … What is it? … I didn't hear anything … Nonsense …

The door opens. Badger and Mole rush in

BADGER (*his war-cry*) Up the Badger!

MOLE (*his*) A Mole! A Mole!

BADGER (*wielding his cudgel*) Lay in to 'em, boys!

Act 4
Scene 3

Toad of
Toad Hall
– a comedy

STALLS

MOLE (*between blows*) Sorry we're late, Weasel − (*biff*) − but many thanks all the same − (*biff*) − for the kind invitation. (*Biff!*)

CHIEF WEASEL The other door! Quick!

The other door opens, and Toad and Rat charge in

TOAD (*terribly*) I've come home, Weasel.

He makes for him How are *you*? (*Bang!*)

THE ENEMY (*variously*) Help! … Mercy! … All *right*, all right!

BADGER Wallop 'em, boys. Keep walloping!

Some of the enemy are showing fight, some are escaping through the doors and windows, some are begging for mercy with uplifted paws

MOLE (*seeking whom he can devour*) A Mole! A Mole!

(*To an unhappy Stoat*) Hallo, were you looking for anything? (*Biff*) Just wanted to say goodbye? (*Biff*) Goodbye! (*Biff*) Sorry you can't stop.

He biffs him out of the door

BADGER (*walloping the last of the others out of the window*) There! That's the lot!

He wipes his brow A pity! I was just beginning to enjoy it.

RAT They've surrendered.

BADGER   Now then, Toad, stir your stumps, and look lively.
I want some grub, I do. We've got your house
back for you, and you don't offer us so much as a
sandwich.

RAT (*indicating the prisoners*) They'll help you get it ready, Toady.

TOAD (*reluctantly*) Oh, all right.

MOLE (*to Toad, as the others go out*)
Don't forget the wine, Toad. We shall want to
drink your health, and you'll have to make a
speech.

TOAD (*cheering up*) Oh, right, right. That's all right, leave that to me.

*He leaves, singing happily to himself. Badger, Mole and Rat sit down to await his return, all
smiling broadly.*

32